THIS BOOK IS FOR ....

children of primary school age who have learnt
the basic notes of the descant (soprano) recorder up
to E, ten notes above written Middle C, and who are
looking for interesting and enjoyable music to play
by themselves or with their friends. The main aim of
the book is to help children to perform *musically*,
with feeling and with a sense of character. This is
where Pooh and his companions will make it easy
because the player will have to capture the sadness
of Eeyore, the bustle of Rabbit, the bounce of
Tigger and the *buzz! buzz! buzz!* of bees round the
honey tree.

Before each piece, there are a few words of advice
on how to play the music and to help with particular
technical difficulties. Also, at the beginning of the
book, there is a list with definitions of all the
musical signs and expressions used. Finally, the last
three pieces are for more than one recorder and
these should provide an excellent introduction to
part-playing.

I very much hope that *The Pooh Recorder Book* will
bring pleasure and help to children learning to play
the descant recorder whether at home or at school.

Philip Stott

THE POOH RECORDER BOOK

Original and easy pieces for descant recorder

MUSIC AND ADVICE BY
Philip Stott

Inspired by Winnie-the-Pooh and The House at Pooh Corner
by A.A.Milne

Illustrated by Ernest H. Shepard

Methuen Children's Books

I am grateful to Mrs Valerie Dyke for
checking through the final draft
and to my own daughters, Katherine and Emily,
and Elizabeth and Hilary Newman
for being the first to try out the music.

First published in Great Britain in 1985
by Methuen Children's Books Ltd,
11 New Fetter Lane, London EC4P 4EE
Music and instructions copyright © 1985 by Philip Stott

Reproduced, printed and bound in Great Britain by
Hazell Watson & Viney Limited,
Member of the BPCC Group,
Aylesbury, Bucks

ISBN 0 416 54280 8

CONTENTS

Pooh

THE MUSICAL SIGNS AND EXPRESSIONS USED

You should turn back to this page if you meet a musical sign or expression with which you are not familiar.

Signs	
𝄞⁸	**Treble clef**: the little figure *8* placed over the treble clef tells you that your descant recorder will actually sound one octave (eight notes) higher than the written notes. The descant recorder is thus a *transposing* instrument.
✓	A **breathing mark**: take a breath at the places indicated by this sign.
(✓)	An **optional breathing mark**: only take a breath here if it is absolutely necessary to do so.
♩♩	A curved line linking two or more notes of a different pitch is a **slur**: only tongue the first note; the others then follow smoothly on.
♩˙ , ♩	*Staccato*: a dot over or under a note means that the note is to be played short and detached; tongue '*dot*' or for a crisp *staccato*, '*tut*'.
♩⁻ , ♩	A note with a **dash** over or under it should be slightly stressed.
>	An **accent sign**: the note should be strongly accentuated.
♩〰♩	A *glissando* or **slide**: see *Buzz! Buzz! Buzz!*.
♫♫ 3	**Triplets**: a triplet consists of three notes played in the time usually taken by two of the same value. See *The Expotition March*.

⌢		A **pause** or *fermata*: the note or rest over which it is placed should be held a little longer than usual, according to personal taste.
𝄆⋮⋮⋮𝄇		The **repeat sign**: repeat the section of music between the dotted bar lines.
1 **2**		**First** and **second time bars**: omit the first and play the second after the repeat.
<		A **hairpin** sign meaning becoming gradually louder.
>		A **hairpin** sign meaning becoming gradually softer.
Expressions	*pp*	Abbreviation for *pianissimo*, Italian for very soft.
	p	Abbreviation for *piano* or soft.
	mp	Abbreviation for *mezzo-piano* or moderately soft.
	mf	Abbreviation for *mezzo-forte* or moderately loud.
	f	Abbreviation for *forte* or loud.
	ff	Abbreviation for *fortissimo* or very loud (but do not overblow and make your instrument sharp and out of tune).
a tempo or *a tempo primo*		Go back to the original speed or pace of the music.
più mosso		More movement or a little quicker.
poco rit.		Slow down a little.
rit.		Abbreviation for *ritardando*, Italian for becoming gradually slower.
senza rit.		Without slowing down; keep the pace up.
sonore		Full-toned; make the music sound out.

POOH'S EXERCISE MUSIC FOR REMOVING STOUTNESS

The first four bars of the music are Pooh's theme tune and this tune will be repeated in some form wherever Pooh appears in the book. Try to make the music sound as if Pooh is stumping along, whistling happily to himself.

A note with a dash over or under it ($\bar{\rho}$, $\underline{\rho}$) should be slightly stressed; a note with a dot over or under it ($\dot{\rho}$, $\dot{\rho}$) should be played *staccato*, or short and detached (for example, ρ equals ρ). You will achieve *staccato* playing by tonguing the word *dot*. A note with an accent sign (>) over or under it should be strongly stressed.

Poor Pooh is unable to touch his toes — try to catch this feeling in your playing.

'*Tra-la-la, tra-la-la*, as he stretched up as high as he could go, and then *Tra-la-la, tra-la-oh, help! -la*, as he tried to reach his toes.'

Stumpily

Tra - la -la, Tra - la - la, Tra - la   oh, help! la

Tra - la -la, Tra - la - la

Rum - tum - tid - dle - um - tum

9

RABBIT'S REEL

A reel is a quick dance of Scandinavian origin that is very popular in Scotland, Ireland and North America (e.g. the Virginia reel). It is usually in 4/4 time and is danced by two or more couples, thus being very suitable for busy Rabbit and his many friends-and-relations, including Small (when found!)

Rabbit's reel is written in what we call *alla breve* time, indicated by the sign ¢ . This is really 2/2 time and means that, although the piece looks as if it is in 4/4 time, it should be played quickly enough to feel only 2 minim (half-note) beats in each bar. These will fall on the first and third crotchets (quarter-notes). At first, however, it might be easier to count it in 4 crotchets. Note the change of key in the sixth bar.

The first bar, with its crotchet triplets, is easy if you play it as 'Come to the Fair', the first beat being on 'Come' and the second on 'Fair'. (See *The Expotition March* if you want to know more about triplets).

10

Busily

senza rit.   *poco rit.*

PIGLET'S RAIN MUSIC

(for playing when becoming entirely surrounded by water)

'It rained and
it rained and it rained.'

This is Piglet's *Rain Music* and it will help you to practise your *staccato* playing; remember to tongue *dot* for the *staccato* notes. The rain should fall steadily, but not too fast. Make the 'Help! Help!' nice and loud as Piglet becomes a 'little Anxious to be a Very Small Animal Entirely Surrounded by Water'.

The first two bars are Piglet's very own theme tune; this is *not* played *staccato*.

Carelessly

Steady rain! (Not too fast)

mf

mp

Pit, pat, pat

ff Help! Help!

mf

ff

mf

mp

f

KANGA'S AND ROO'S JUMPING TUNE

This is Kanga's and Roo's *Jumping Tune* and you must play it with a good deal of bounce, stressing the notes with an accent sign (>). The main tune is for Kanga and should be rather slow and deliberate; the middle section, marked *più mosso*, is for Roo and this should be much quicker and lighter. The words *più mosso* mean 'more movement' or a little quicker. *A tempo primo* means return to the original, first, speed of the music. Don't fall in a mouse-hole!

Note: Careful timing of the dotted quaver and the following semiquaver will help you to achieve the right bounce and spring.

' "Just one more jump dear, and then we must go home." '

At a slow bounce (matronly)

Più mosso (Roo-speed)

a tempo primo

rit.------------------------

rit.------------------------------

THE WORRA-WORRA-WORRA JIG

(for Tigger)

A jig is a lively jumping dance that suits Tigger's bouncy nature very well. You should play 'The *Worraworraworra* Jig' as if Tigger is bouncing Eeyore into the river (especially the jumpy passages in bars 8 and 24).

To make Tigger's *worraworraworra*, you should play loudly (but do not overblow) and only tongue the first note of the slurred semiquavers (sixteenth-notes), stressing the notes with the accent sign (>) as you play. Slow down (*rit.*) when even Tigger collapses at the end.

'But whatever his weight in pounds, shillings, and ounces, He always seems bigger because of his bounces.'

16

rit. ---

EEYORE'S LAMENT

Eeyore, the old grey Donkey, is a very gloomy animal who lives in a rather boggy part of the Forest. This is his lament or sad song.

To get the 'Ee-yore' sound out of your recorder, you should stress the note with the accent sign (>) and slur it onto the low D which follows (i.e. do not tongue the D).

Watch out for the F♯s and the E♮ in the last part of the lament.

Make the tune sound as if everybody has forgotten Eeyore's Birthday.

POOHSTICKS IDYLL

An idyll is a piece of music of a quiet, pastoral nature recalling the peace of the countryside. This idyll is for a gentle summer afternoon on the Poohsticks Bridge. Try to make the river slip slowly by and feel the warmth of the summer air in the Forest. You will have to phrase the music very carefully and make sure that you only tongue the first of the slurred notes. Play smoothly and gently throughout.

19

'THE FLOATING BEAR' HORNPIPE

A hornpipe is a lively English dance, sometimes associated with sailors, like Pooh! The name may recall the fact that the music was originally played on a pipe made from animal's horn, although we are not certain about this.

Old-style hornpipes tended to have three beats in each bar. *'The Floating Bear' Hornpipe* is in this form because it is written in 3/2 time. This means that there are 3 minims (half-notes) in each bar, like this:

At first, you might prefer to count 6 crotchet (quarter-note) beats in each bar.

Later hornpipes have 2 or 4 beats to the bar.

Play Pooh's hornpipe quickly and look out for his theme tune.

Paddling vigorously

OWL'S FANCY
or WOL'S DELIGHT

(for players of some brain)

Owl, being a bird of some education who can spell his own name WOL, is not content with nice, easy time-signatures and you will have to try your hand at 5/4 time in his piece. This means that there are five crotchet (quarter-note) beats in each bar, like this:

It is rather like playing a piece with a mixture of bars of 2/4 and 3/4 time. If you play the slurred notes properly it will help you get the feel of the music, which is very serious and learned!

Owl-like   ✓ **With wisdom and dignity**

Oo-oo o-ooo!

rit.

BUZZ!BUZZ!BUZZ!

*(for 2 descant recorders
and a blue balloon)*

'Isn't it funny
How a bear likes honey?
Buzz! Buzz! Buzz!
I wonder why he does?'

This is a 'fun' piece for two descant recorders and a large *blue* balloon (if available). You will also need a sharp pin!

The second descant recorder player should tie the balloon to the end of his or her recorder with a little thread and then, when the time comes (in the next-to-the-last bar), he or she should help Christopher Robin 'pop' the balloon by using the pin. The first descant recorder will make Pooh float down by a *glissando* or 'slide'. To play this, you should finger the top D as normal and then, still playing strongly, *slide* your fingers and thumb on to the recorder to produce the low G (with a bump!) If you don't have a balloon or you are too frightened to 'pop' one, stamp your foot or make a popping noise with your mouth instead.

You must also find Pooh's theme, play like bees and float like a cloud!

ff   TAKE PIN   AND   POP!   ff

THE WOOZLE HUNTING ROUND

' "No," said Pooh, "because it makes different marks. It is either Two Woozles and one, as it might be, Wizzle, or Two, as it might be, Wizzles and one, if so it is, Woozle. Let us continue to follow them." '

A 'round' is a short but perpetual piece of music in which each voice enters in turn and usually at the same pitch — just like the woozles *and/or* wizzles tracked by Pooh and Piglet when they were going round the spinney one fine winter's day.

This round captures the woozles' hunting calls (but not the woozles!). First there is one woozle, then a second and, finally, a wizzle makes its presence felt. After you have got going, you can repeat the passage between the repeat marks (∗)

as many times as you like. To finish you may do one of two things:

1. end all together by playing the final chord with a pause mark over it; or,

2. end one by one by turning the G into a dotted minim (half-note) at the points indicated — in the order, first woozle, second woozle and last of all the wizzle.

Good tracking.

Note: this was to have been a picture of a woozle or a wizzle, but, unfortunately, Pooh and Piglet never caught up with one.

*Repeat as often as you like!

Then finish *either:*

1) all together on the last bar,
or:

2) separately at the dotted minim (𝅗𝅥.)

notes above or below the stave.
End in the order listed (1 to 3).

THE EXPOTITION MARCH

'They all went off to discover the Pole,
  Owl and Piglet and Rabbit and all;
It's a thing you Discover, as I've been
      tole
  By Owl and Piglet and Rabbit and
      all.'

The lively *Expotition March* is for three descant recorder players who must tune their instruments very carefully or the music will not sound at all pleasing. Try to keep together by counting very carefully and by listening to each other. You should also make the animals' theme tunes (first Pooh, then 'Owl and Piglet and Rabbit and all') sound like their owners.

Above all, this piece will help you to play **triplets** correctly. A triplet consists of three notes played in the time usually taken by two of the same value. The number *3* is placed over or under the group to show the change, like this:

To help you play the triplets in the *Expotition March*, try saying the following phrase quickly and then repeating it on your recorder:

Eat   Straw-ber-ry Jam   Pie

Come on!

Come on!

Come on!

Briskly

31